THE DON'T LAUGH CHALLENGE

CHALLENGE®

Joke Book

TEEN EDITION

A Side-Splitting Hilarious Joke Book for Teenagers and Tweens

TM & Copyright© 2020 by Bacchus Publishing House

ALL RIGHTS RESERVED.

Published in the United States. By purchase of this book, you have been licensed one copy for personal use only. No part of this work may be reproduced, redistributed, or used in any form or by any means without prior written permission of the publisher and copyright owner.
The Don't Laugh Challenge®

TX 8-837-630

TX 8-837-124

www.dontlaughchallenge.com

DON'T LAUGH CHALLENGE®
BONUS PLAY

JOIN OUR JOKE CLUB AND GET THE BONUS PLAY PDF!

★ ★ ★ ★ ★ ★ ★ ★ ★ ★ ★ ★

SIMPLY SEND US AN EMAIL TO:

 **BACCHUSPUBLISH@GMAIL.COM**

AND YOU WILL GET THE FOLLOWING:

- **10 BONUS HILARIOUS JOKES!**
- **AN ENTRY IN OUR MONTHLY GIVEAWAY OF A $25 AMAZON GIFT CARD!**

WE DRAW A NEW WINNER EACH MONTH AND WILL CONTACT YOU VIA EMAIL!

GOOD LUCK!

:)

Welcome to
The Don't Laugh Challenge®

• How do you play?

The Don't Laugh Challenge is made up of 10 rounds with 2 games in each round. It is a 2-3 player game with the players being 'Teen #1', 'Teen #2', and a 'King' or 'Queen'. In each game you have an opportunity to score points by making the other players laugh.

After completing each round, tally up the points to determine the Round Champion! Add all 10 rounds together to see who is the Ultimate Don't Laugh Challenge Master! If you end up in a tie, use our final Tie-Breaker Round for a Winner Takes All!

• Who can play the game?

Get the whole family involved! Grab a family member or a friend and take turns going back and forth. We've also added Bonus Points in game 2, so grab a 3rd person, a.k.a 'King' or 'Queen', and earn an extra point by making them guess your scene!

The Don't Laugh Challenge® Activity Rules

- ## Game 1 - Jokes (1 point each)

  Teen #1 will hold the book and read each joke to Teen #2. If the joke makes Teen #2 laugh, Teen #1 can record a point for the joke. Each joke is worth 1 point. At the end of the jokes, tally up your total Joke Points scored for Teen #1 and continue to Game 2!

- ## Game 2 - Silly Scenarios (2 points each + bonus point)

  Without telling the other Teen what the scenarios say, read each scenario to yourself and then get creative by acting it out! You can use sound effects, but be sure not to say any words! If you make the other Teen laugh, record your points and continue to the next scenario.

  BONUS POINT: Get your parents or a third player, a.k.a King or Queen, involved and have them guess what in the world you are doing! Get the King or Queen to guess the scene correctly and you score a BONUS POINT!

The Don't Laugh Challenge®
Activity Rules

Once Teen #1 completes both games it is Teen #2's turn. The directions at the bottom of the book will tell you who goes next. Once you have both completed all the games in the round, add your total points from each game to the Round Score Page and record the Round winner!

- ## How do you get started?

Flip a coin. If guessed correctly, then that Teen begins!

Tip:

Make any of the activities extra funny by using facial expressions, funny voices or silly movements!

JOKES

WHAT DID THE GUITAR SAY TO THE UKULELE?

"UKE, I AM YOUR FATHER."

_____ /1

WHO'S THE POOREST RAPPER IN THE GAME?

50 CENT.

_____ /1

WHY DON'T TEENS SLEEP VERY MUCH?

IT'S COOLER TO BE WOKE.

_____ /1

WHO LOVES TO TALK AND IS FRIENDS WITH BASICALLY EVERYONE?

ALEXA.

_____ /1

JOKES TOTAL: _____ /4

TEEN 1 CONTINUE TO THE NEXT PAGE →

JOKES

WHAT'S A TEEN'S FAVORITE CRAFT?

MINECRAFT.

___ /1

WHICH HERO SHRINKS WHEN HE LACKS CONFIDENCE?

CAN'T MAN.

___ /1

WHAT DO YOU CALL AN ANIMAL THAT'S ALWAYS SENDING PICS TO FRIENDS?

SNAP-CAT-TER.

___ /1

WHAT DO YOU CALL A YOUNG ADULT WHO LIKES *STAR WARS?*

___ /1

A MILLENNIAL FALCON.

JOKES TOTAL: ___ /4

PASS THE BOOK TO TEEN 2 →

13

JOKES

WHAT DO YOU CALL IT WHEN A KID NEEDS TO GO TO THE BATHROOM?

/1

CALL OF DOODY.

WHY IS IT HARD TO TEXT SPIRITS?

/1

THEY ALWAYS GHOST YOU!

HOW DOES HARRY POTTER TEXT HIS FRIENDS?

/1

THROUGH SNAPE-CHAT.

WHY DO RIGHT ANGLES LOVE TO GO TO THE BEACH?

/1

BECAUSE THEY LOVE 90° WEATHER!

JOKES TOTAL: /4

TEEN 2 CONTINUE TO THE NEXT PAGE →

14

JOKES

WHY DON'T PEOPLE LIKE PLAYING CARDS WITH THE TIGER KING?

HE'S KNOWN TO BE A CHEETAH!

/1

WHY DID THE MATH BOOK GO SEE THE THERAPIST?

IT HAD WAY TOO MANY PROBLEMS!

/1

WHY DID THE MUSIC FAN RUN UP ON STAGE?

THEY WERE TRYING TO 'STAN' OUT!

/1

WHAT IS A TREE'S FAVORITE DESSERT?

ROOT BEER FLOATS.

/1

JOKES TOTAL: /4

TIME TO ADD UP YOUR POINTS! →

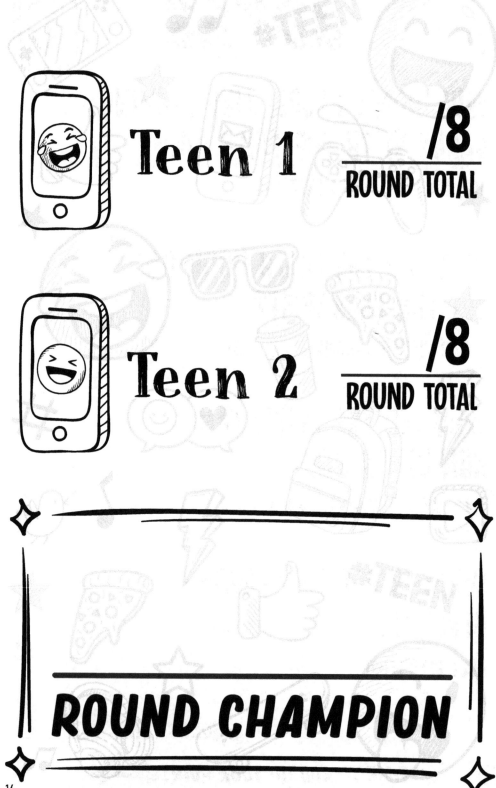

Teen 1   /8
ROUND TOTAL

Teen 2   /8
ROUND TOTAL

ROUND CHAMPION

ROUND 2

JOKES

WHAT DO YOU CALL IT WHEN TAYLOR SWIFT'S FAN BASE GROWS 4x ITS SIZE?

/1

SQUAD-RUPLES.

WHY IS IT HARD TO TRUST A BEAUTICIAN?

/1

THEY WEAR SO MANY MASQUES!

WHAT WOULD YOU CALL A SHOW ABOUT HERMIONE ON NETFLIX?

/1

GRANGER THINGS.

HOW DID THE CLOCK GO VIRAL?

/1

BY USING TIKTOK!

JOKES TOTAL: /4

TEEN 1 CONTINUE TO THE NEXT PAGE ➞

JOKES

HOW DID THE CHIA SEED BECOME THE NEW PRESIDENT?

THEY SUPERSEDED THE OLD ONE!

/1

WHY DO TEENS STILL LIKE ICE CUBE?

HE'S PRETTY CHILL.

/1

WHAT DID BABY GROOT CALL HIMSELF BEFORE HE WAS BABY GROOT?

"I AM ROOT!"

/1

WHERE IS THE BEST PLACE TO SPEND THANKSGIVING?

TURKEY.

/1

JOKES TOTAL: _____ /4

PASS THE BOOK TO TEEN 2 ➡

19

JOKES

WHY ARE PIGS SO POPULAR IN JUNIOR HIGH SCHOOL?

THEY ALWAYS GO HAM!

/1

WHAT'S THE BEST WAY TO PUSH SOMEONE'S BUTTONS?

HACK THEIR COMPUTER.

/1

HOW ARE TEENS SIMILAR TO MOTION SENSOR LIGHTS?

THEY BOTH GET TRIGGERED EASILY.

/1

WHY ARE SCHOOLS STOCKED WITH LIQUIDS?

/1

TEENS ARE KNOWN TO BE THIRSTY...

JOKES TOTAL: /4

TEEN 2 CONTINUE TO THE NEXT PAGE ➡

JOKES

WHY DO FORTNITE BOYS SMELL FUNNY?

THEY ALWAYS PICK AXE!

/1

WHAT TYPE OF NET IS USED TO CATCH A GOOD TIME?

NETFLIX.

/1

HOW DO STUDENTS DEAL WITH BEEF AT SCHOOL?

THEY EAT.

/1

WHAT KIND OF CANDY IS BEST WHEN WRAPPED?

/1

EMINEMS.

JOKES TOTAL: _____ /4

TIME TO ADD UP YOUR POINTS! ➡

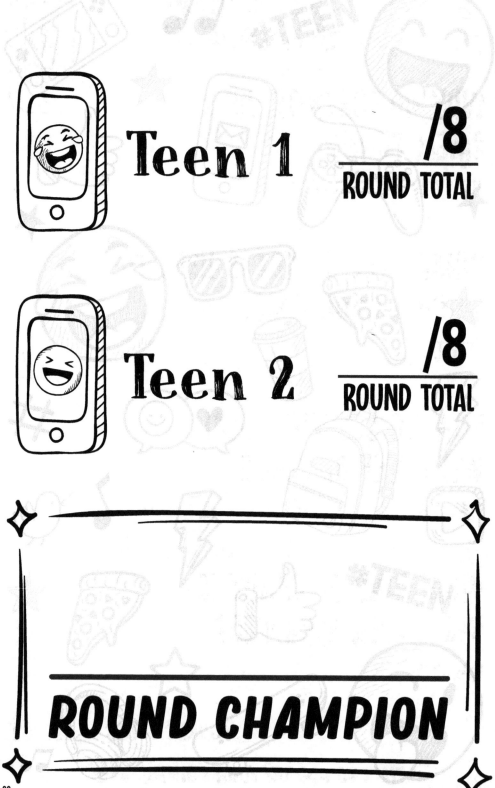

Teen 1   /8
ROUND TOTAL

Teen 2   /8
ROUND TOTAL

ROUND CHAMPION

ROUND 3

JOKES

WHY DO SOME BEAUTY VLOGGERS NOT TURN IN THEIR ASSIGNMENTS?

/1

THEY LIKE DOING MAKE-UP WORK!

WHAT'S A SCOOTER KID'S WEAKNESS?

/1

THE SHINS!

HOW DO YOU KNOW HOW SOMEONE IS FEELING?

/1

YOU JUST CHECK THEIR EMOJIS.

WHAT DO YOU GET WHEN YOU CROSS A VSCO GIRL WITH TACO BELL?

/1

A SCRUNCHY TACO!

JOKES TOTAL: /4

TEEN 1 CONTINUE TO THE NEXT PAGE →

JOKES

WHAT TYPE OF VEHICLE HAS THE COOLEST NAME?

VANS.

/1

HOW COME TEENS CAN'T SNEAK LIQUIDS INTO EVENTS?

THEIR HYDRO FLASKS ARE TOO BIG!

/1

WHAT'S THE BIGGEST FEAR OF TEENS TODAY?

F.O.M.O.

/1

HOW DO TEENS MAKE S'MORES?

WITH MARSHMALLOWS & INSTA-GRAHAM CRACKERS!

/1

JOKES TOTAL: /4

PASS THE BOOK TO TEEN 2 ➡

JOKES

WHAT CREATURE EXISTS ON THE INTERNET, BUT NOT IN REAL LIFE?

A TROLL.

/1

HOW DO TEENS MAKE THE PERFECT COFFEE?

BY USING MULTIPLE FILTERS!

/1

WHAT KIND OF DOCS DO STUDENTS TRUST THE MOST?

GOOGLE DOCS.

/1

WHY DO THE MAJORITY OF POPULAR SONGS SEEM VIOLENT?

/1

BECAUSE THEY SLAP!

JOKES TOTAL: /4

TEEN 2 CONTINUE TO THE NEXT PAGE ➞

JOKES

WHAT HAPPENS IF YOU DON'T TIE YOUR SHOE IN SPRING?
YOU FIND YOURSELF IN FALL!

_____ /1

HOW DO SKATERS LIKE THEIR CHICKEN WINGS?
BONELESS.

_____ /1

WHAT'S THE FASTEST DELIVERY SERVICE IN THE OCEAN?
SEA URGENT.

_____ /1

WHAT DO YOU CALL A GROUP OF COLLEGE STUDENTS WHO ALL DRINK COFFEE TOGETHER?

_____ /1

A FRAP-TERNITY!

JOKES TOTAL: _____ /4

TIME TO ADD UP YOUR POINTS! ➡️

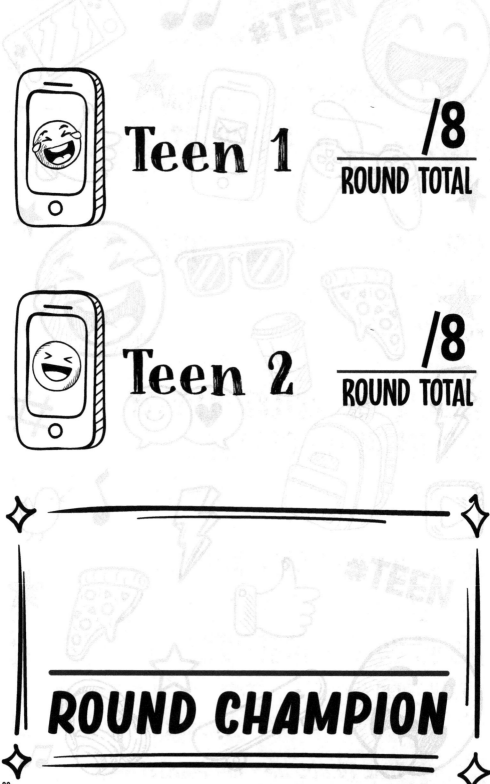

Teen 1 **/8**
ROUND TOTAL

Teen 2 **/8**
ROUND TOTAL

ROUND CHAMPION

JOKES

WHAT DO YOU CALL A FOOD FIGHT IN 2020?

GAME OF THROWN.

_____ /1

WHY DID THE BOY STOP WATCHING THE MURDER MYSTERY SHOW ABOUT THE MUSICAL INSTRUMENTS?

HE THOUGHT IT WAS MUCH TOO VIOLIN-T!

_____ /1

HOW DO YOU DECORATE A GAMER'S BIRTHDAY PARTY?

ALL YOU HAVE TO DO IS FILL THE ROOM WITH STREAMERS!

_____ /1

WHY DO SOME TEENS PLAY HOPSCOTCH DURING BREAK?

_____ /1

THEY LOVE SKIPPING SCHOOL!

JOKES TOTAL: _____ /4

TEEN 1 CONTINUE TO THE NEXT PAGE →

JOKES

WHY DID THE PHONE NOT WANT TO GO ON THE CRUISE SHIP?

IT WAS AFRAID IT WOULD SYNC!

_/1

WHAT DO YOU CALL IT WHEN NICKI MINAJ TUTORS YOU?

HOME-TWERK.

_/1

WHY ARE TEENS FEELING #BLESSED?

'CAUSE MOST OF THEM WEAR HOLY JEANS!

_/1

HOW DO YOU KNOW WHEN THE ALPHABET IS SPREADING GOSSIP?

_/1

IT SPILLS THE T!

JOKES TOTAL: _/4

PASS THE BOOK TO TEEN 2 ➜

JOKES

WHO IS A REPTILE'S FAVORITE SINGER?

LIZZ-ARD-O.

/1

WHY WAS THE DJ SUCH A BAD GARDENER?

HE ALWAYS LET THE BEET DROP!

/1

IF THE WIZARD'S CUP IS JUST FOR WIZARDS, WHAT DOES EVERYONE ELSE GET?

MUG-GLES!

/1

WHAT IS LUKE SKYWALKER'S FAVORITE FRUIT?

/1

BANANA-KIN.

JOKES TOTAL: /4

TEEN 2 CONTINUE TO THE NEXT PAGE →

JOKES

WHAT DID THE POPCORN SAY TO THE MOVIE THEATRE?

"WE'RE BUTTER TOGETHER." ___/1

WHAT GAME HAS NO KILLER BUT FIVE DIE, AND IF ALL FIVE ARE THE SAME, YOU YELL ITS NAME?

YAHTZEE! ___/1

HOW DOES POST MALONE ENERGIZE HIS HOUSE?

SUN-POWER. ___/1

WHY COULDN'T THE BOY SEND THE LETTER?

___/1

IT WAS STATIONERY!

JOKES TOTAL: ___/4

TIME TO ADD UP YOUR POINTS! ➜

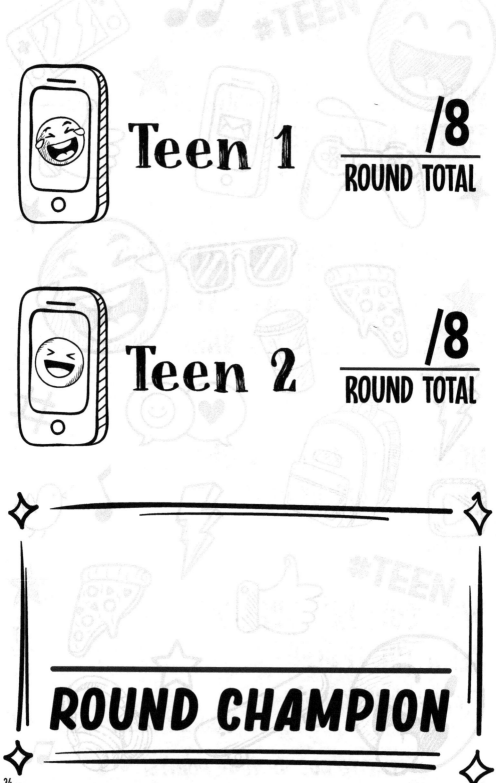

Teen 1   /8
          ROUND TOTAL

Teen 2   /8
          ROUND TOTAL

ROUND CHAMPION

34

ROUND
5

JOKES

WHY WAS THE RAPPER SO COLD?

THEY HAD TOO MUCH ICE ON THEIR WRIST!

/1

WHICH AVENGER IS THE HARDEST TO SEE THROUGH?

BLACK WINDOW.

/1

WHY DOES EVERYONE THINK THAT THE TEEN SEAMSTRESS HAS AN ATTITUDE?

SHE'S ALWAYS ASKING, *"SEW WHAT?"*

/1

WHAT GROUP LED THE WAR BETWEEN FRUITS AND VEGETABLES?

THE APPLE CORPS.

/1

JOKES TOTAL: /4

TEEN 1 CONTINUE TO THE NEXT PAGE →

JOKES

WHY DO BASEBALL PLAYERS VISIT CAVES SO OFTEN?

THEY'RE ALWAYS IN NEED OF MORE BATS!

_____ /1

WHAT'S VAN HELSING'S FAVORITE MEAL?

STAKE WITH GARLIC.

_____ /1

WHY COULDN'T THE CLARINET PLAY MUSIC?

IT DIDN'T KNOW HOW TO REED.

_____ /1

HOW DO THE AVENGERS FIND SYNONYMS?

_____ /1

THEY CHECK WITH THE THE-THOR-US.

JOKES TOTAL: _____ /4

PASS THE BOOK TO TEEN 2 ➜

JOKES

WHAT DID THE TEENAGER SAY WHEN ASKED IF THEY WANTED TO PLAY POKER?

/1

"BET!"

HOW DO LAWYERS GET WHAT THEY WANT?

/1

THEY USE PLEAS.

WHAT IS THE SUIT'S FAVORITE TV SHOW?

/1

TIE-GER KING.

WHY WAS IT HARD TO MAKE PLANS WITH THE EXPENSIVE WATCH?

/1

IT WAS NEVER FREE!

JOKES TOTAL: /4

TEEN 2 CONTINUE TO THE NEXT PAGE →

JOKES

WHICH INDIE-POPSTAR WEARS THE MOST MASCARA?

BILLIE EYELASH.

/1

WHAT PRANK DO WIZARDS LIKE TO PLAY?

DING-DONG QUID-DITCH!

/1

WHY DO PEOPLE WHO SEND FLOWERS FIND DANCE DATES EASILY?

BECAUSE THEY ROSE TO THE OCCASION!

/1

WHAT DID THE TAXI DRIVER SAY WHEN THE PASSENGER PAID IN BUTTONS?

/1

"HEY! THAT'S NOT FARE!"

JOKES TOTAL: /4

TIME TO ADD UP YOUR POINTS! ➡️

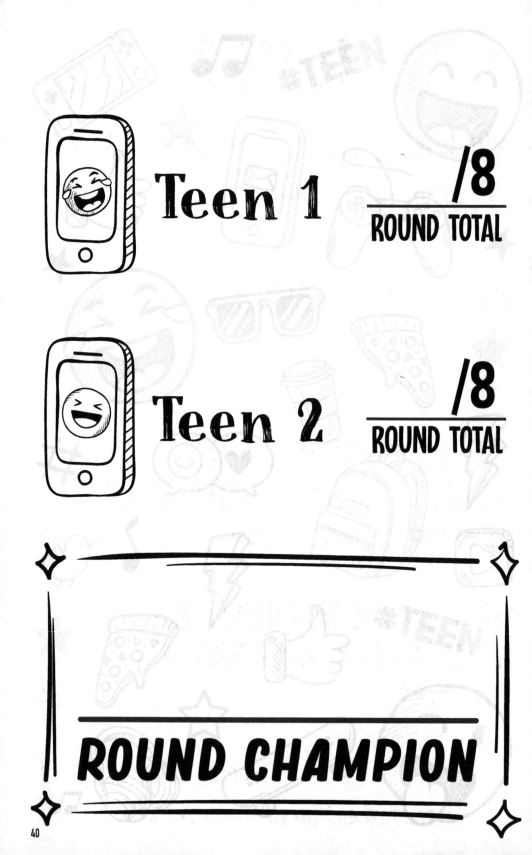

Teen 1 /8
ROUND TOTAL

Teen 2 /8
ROUND TOTAL

ROUND CHAMPION

ROUND
6

JOKES

WHAT DID THE CONFUSED MATHEMATICIAN ASK AFTER GETTING THE MEDIAN?

"BUT WHAT DO YOU *MEAN*?!"

/1

WHAT DO YOU CALL IT WHEN A PRINTER PLAYS MUSIC?

PAPER JAM!

/1

WHICH DINOSAUR HAS THE BEST GOSSIP AND LOVES TO SHOW IT OFF?

THE TEA-FLEX.

/1

WHAT SIZE COFFEE DO POPSTARS ORDER?

/1

ARIANA GRANDE.

JOKES TOTAL: /4

TEEN 1 CONTINUE TO THE NEXT PAGE ➜

JOKES

WHY DID THE NEUTRON GET EVERYTHING FOR FREE?

HE WAS NEVER CHARGED!

/1

WHAT IS A DONUT'S FAVORITE MATTHEW MCCONAUGHEY MOVIE?

GLAZED AND CONFUSED.

/1

WHAT DO YOU CALL A SECRET SOCIETY OF BABY HORSES?

A COLT.

/1

WHY DIDN'T ANYONE WANT TO OPEN THE SHOCKED SODA?

/1

BECAUSE IT WAS SHOOK!

JOKES TOTAL: /4

PASS THE BOOK TO TEEN 2 ➡️

JOKES

WHAT DID GROOT SAY AFTER HE SPROUTED AN APPLE?

"I AM FRUIT!"

/1

WHY WERE PEOPLE GIVING THE GAMER CHAPSTICK?

HE SAID THEY WERE CRACKED!

/1

WHAT BIRD JUST STOPPED CRYING?

THE BAWLED EAGLE.

/1

WHY DO TEENS LOVE PEOPLE BEHIND THEM?

THEY'RE ALWAYS BEGGING FOR FOLLOWERS!

/1

JOKES TOTAL: /4

TEEN 2 CONTINUE TO THE NEXT PAGE ➙

JOKES

WHAT DO YOU CALL IT WHEN CELEBRITIES FIGHT?

STAR WARS.

/1

WHY DO TEENS DROP GUITARS SO OFTEN?

'CAUSE THEY LOVE HEARING THE BASS DROP!

/1

WHAT KIND OF VISION DOES EVERY KID WANT?

TELEVISION.

/1

WHAT DO YOU CALL SOMEONE WHO BECOMES A GRANDMA QUICKLY?

INSTA-GRAM.

/1

JOKES TOTAL: /4

TIME TO ADD UP YOUR POINTS! ➡

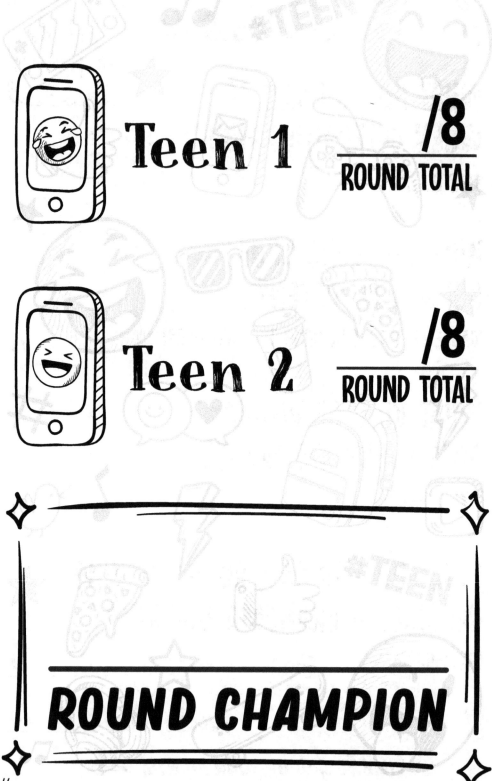

Teen 1 /8
ROUND TOTAL

Teen 2 /8
ROUND TOTAL

ROUND CHAMPION

ROUND 7

JOKES

WHAT KIND OF BOX DO TEENS LOVE PLAYING WITH?

XBOX.

/1

WHY DO ADULTS THINK TEENS DON'T UNDERSTAND STYLE?

THEY'RE ALWAYS ASKING, "WHAT'S GUCCI?"

/1

WHAT'S A TEEN'S "LAST STRAW"?

THEIR METAL ONE!

/1

WHAT'S A POPULAR ACTIVITY BETWEEN FRIENDS LATELY?

HULU HOOP.

/1

JOKES TOTAL: _____ /4

TEEN 1 CONTINUE TO THE NEXT PAGE →

JOKES

WHY DO SOME RAP SONGS SMELL FUNNY?

THERE ARE SO MANY FEATS!

/1

WHAT'S A TEEN'S FAVORITE FRUIT?

LULU LEMONS.

/1

WHY DO SOME GAMERS FEEL LIKE ANGELS?

THEY ALWAYS HAVE HALO!

/1

WHAT DID THE SCIENTIST SAY WHEN THEY ACCIDENTALLY CREATED AN IRON MAN KNOCKOFF?

/1

"AU, MAN!"

JOKES TOTAL: /4

PASS THE BOOK TO TEEN 2 →

49

JOKES

WHAT DO YOU CALL IT WHEN TWO APES ARE THROWING BANANAS AT EACH OTHER?

GORILLA WARFARE.

/1

WHY DO HARDCORE GAMERS NOT LIKE THE OUTDOORS?

THEY HATE CAMPERS!

/1

WHAT KIND OF STOCKS ARE TEENS INTERESTED IN?

BIRKENSTOCKS.

/1

WHAT DO YOU CALL THE SHOW WHERE EVERYONE STANDS STILL?

AMERICAN IDLE.

/1

JOKES TOTAL: /4

TEEN 2 CONTINUE TO THE NEXT PAGE →

JOKES

WHY WAS EVERYONE WORRIED AFTER THE TEEN HEARD A JOKE?

HE KEPT SAYING, *"I'M DEAD!"*

/1

HOW DO YOU KNOW THERE IS A FIRE NEARBY?

YOU'LL HEAR, *"IT'S LIT!"*

/1

WHAT'S A TEEN'S FAVORITE CLASS IN SCHOOL?

SOCIAL MEDIA STUDIES.

/1

WHICH AVENGER LIKES APPLE JUICE?

/1

THE AMAZING CIDER-MAN.

JOKES TOTAL: _____ /4

TIME TO ADD UP YOUR POINTS! ➡

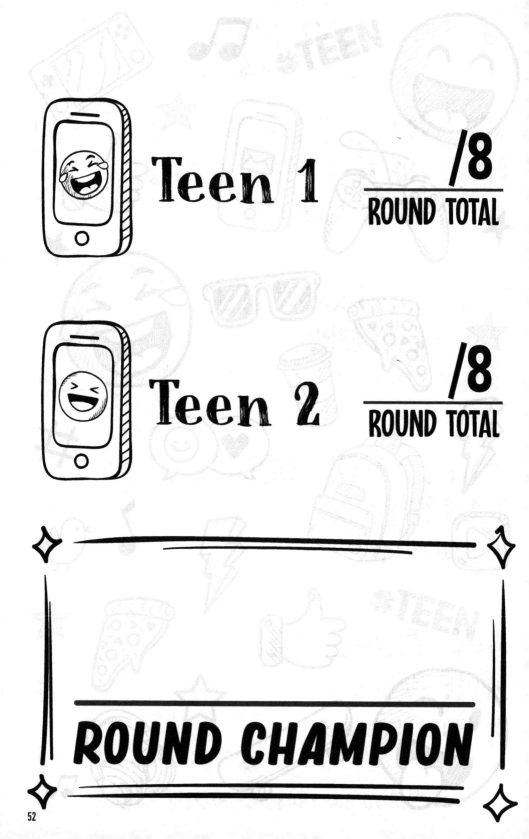

Teen 1   /8
ROUND TOTAL

Teen 2   /8
ROUND TOTAL

ROUND CHAMPION

ROUND 8

JOKES

WHAT'S THE MOST POPULAR TYPE OF SHOP AMONG HIGH SCHOOLERS?

PHOTOSHOP!

/1

WHY ARE TEENS AFRAID TO LOOK UNDER THEIR BED?

BECAUSE OF ALL THE MONSTER CANS!

/1

WHAT DO YOU CALL A GROUP OF SAD MUSICIANS?

TWENTY ONE CRY-LOTS.

/1

WHICH POPSTAR CAN EASILY BECOME A TWO-PERSON ACT?

DUO LIPA.

/1

JOKES TOTAL: /4

TEEN 1 CONTINUE TO THE NEXT PAGE →

JOKES

WHAT'S THE DIFFERENCE BETWEEN *PANIC! AT THE DISCO* AND A DESCENDING BOULDER?

ONE'S ROCK N' ROLL AND THE
OTHER IS A ROLLIN' ROCK!

_____ /1

WHICH RAPPER SHEDS LIGHT ON STREET CORNERS?

LAMP POST MALONE.

_____ /1

WHY DID THE PALEONTOLOGIST LAUGH AT THE JOKE?

HE FOUND IT HUMERUS!

_____ /1

WHAT DO YOU CALL IT WHEN YOU BUILD A TENT IN THE DARK?

_____ /1

FORTNITE.

JOKES TOTAL: _____ /4

PASS THE BOOK TO TEEN 2 ➙

JOKES

WHAT DOES A GOOD SONG AND GETTING HIT IN THE HEAD HAVE IN COMMON?

THEY'RE BOTH BOPS!

_____ /1

HOW DO TEENS LIKE THEIR GRAVY?

THICC.

_____ /1

WHICH AVENGER DOES HIS BEST IN 2020?

VISION.

_____ /1

WHAT DO YOU CALL A WIZARD WHO TATTLES TO THE TEACHER AT HOGWARTS?

_____ /1

A GOLDEN SNITCH.

JOKES TOTAL: _____ /4

TEEN 2 CONTINUE TO THE NEXT PAGE ➔

JOKES

WHY DO TEENS LOVE SOCCER?
IT'S GOT MAD GOALS!

/1

WHAT IS A TURTLE'S FAVORITE THING TO SEND THEIR FRIENDS?
"SNAP" CHATS!

/1

WHAT DO YOU CALL IT WHEN SOMEONE WINS A LIFETIME SUPPLY OF COFFEE?

/1

WINNING THE LATTE-RY!

WHY ARE TEENS SO SNEAKY?
THEY'RE ALWAYS *LOW KEY* DOING SOMETHING!

/1

JOKES TOTAL: /4

TIME TO ADD UP YOUR POINTS! ➡

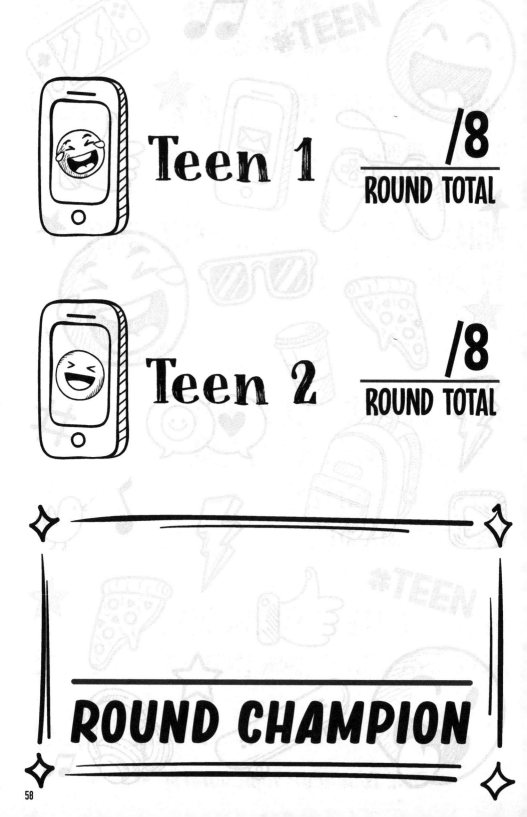

Teen 1 /8
ROUND TOTAL

Teen 2 /8
ROUND TOTAL

ROUND CHAMPION

ROUND
9

JOKES

WHAT DO YOU CALL IT WHEN A SODA DAYDREAMS?

FANTA-SY.

/1

HOW DO YOU WATCH TIKTOK WITHOUT A PHONE?

EASY! LOOK AT THE CLOCK.

/1

WHAT IS AN OWL'S FAVORITE WAY TO WATCH MOVIES?

USING WHO-LU.

/1

WHY DID THE SCHOOL THINK SOMEONE WAS SUPER SICK?

THEY SUDDENLY WENT VIRAL!

/1

JOKES TOTAL: ___ /4

TEEN 1 CONTINUE TO THE NEXT PAGE ➔

JOKES

WHY ARE MOST BLOGGERS GOOD AT GEOMETRY?

THEY KNOW ALL THE GOOD ANGLES!

/1

WHAT'S THE COOLEST WAY TO ORDER TACOS?

SUPREME.

/1

WHY DON'T SOME KIDS READ AT HOME?

THEY ALREADY READ THEIR TEXTS IN CLASS.

/1

WHAT'S THE MODERN-DAY DOUBLE-DOG DARE?

INTERNET CHALLENGES!

/1

JOKES TOTAL: /4

PASS THE BOOK TO TEEN 2 ➔

JOKES

WHAT FORM OF CURRENCY DO TEENS LIKE MOST?

V-BUCKS.

/1

WHY ARE THERE SO MANY DRAWINGS OF PEOPLE AT JUNIOR HIGH SCHOOLS?

CAUSE THERE'S A LOT OF POSERS!

/1

WHAT DO TEENS SAY TO GET SO MANY FRIENDS?

/1

"LIKE AND SUBSCRIBE!"

WHAT'S THE TEEN VERSION OF MARIO BROS?

/1

DUTCH BROS.

JOKES TOTAL: /4

TEEN 2 CONTINUE TO THE NEXT PAGE ➡

JOKES

Teen
2

WHY DO GAMERS ALWAYS KEEP THEIR PHONES ON THEM?

IN CASE THEY GET A CALL OF DUTY!

/1

WHAT DO YOU CALL LUNCH WITH YOUR FRIENDS?

FAM SANDWICH.

/1

WHY DO RAPPERS USE THUNDER IN THEIR SONGS?

BECAUSE THEY ALL USE SOUNDCLOUD!

/1

WHAT DO YOU CALL SOMEONE WHO BORROWS MONEY WITHOUT TELLING ANYONE?

/1

A LOAN WOLF.

JOKES TOTAL: /4

TIME TO ADD UP YOUR POINTS! ➡️

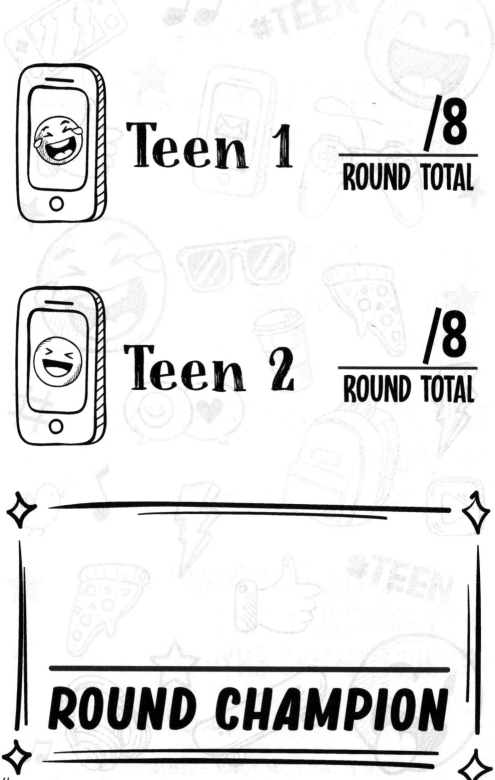

Teen 1 /8
ROUND TOTAL

Teen 2 /8
ROUND TOTAL

ROUND CHAMPION

ROUND
10

JOKES

HOW DOES IRON MAN KNOW HOW TO USE HIS SUIT?

HE READ THE IRON MAN-UAL.

/1

WHY DO TEENS ALWAYS SPILL THEIR COFFEE?

THEY ORDER IT "NO CAP!"

/1

WHAT DO STUDENTS CALL A POWERPOINT SLIDE?

MEMES.

/1

WHICH RAPPER HATES MONDAYS?

THE WEEKND.

/1

JOKES TOTAL: ___ /4

TEEN 1 CONTINUE TO THE NEXT PAGE ➜

JOKES

WHAT IS A FRUIT'S FAVORITE ISLAND?

PAPAYA NEW GUINEA.

_____ /1

WHY DIDN'T THE POST OFFICE SEND THE PROBLEM LETTER?

THEY FELT SOMEONE NEEDED TO ADDRESS IT!

_____ /1

WHAT DO YOU CALL IT WHEN LIN MANUEL MIRANDA SINGS IN THE SHOWER?

A SOAP OPERA!

_____ /1

WHAT DO YOU CALL A DINOSAUR POLICEMAN?

A TRICERA-COP.

_____ /1

JOKES TOTAL: _____ /4

PASS THE BOOK TO TEEN 2 ➝

JOKES

WHAT IS A LIZARD'S FAVORITE KIND OF TRIANGLE?

SCALE-NE.

/1

WHAT DO YOU CALL A PODCAST ABOUT CHIPS?

"NACHO AVERAGE PODCAST!"

/1

WHAT'S CAPTAIN AMERICA'S FAVORITE PART OF A CAR?

THE WIND-SHIELD.

/1

WHAT IS A RAPPER'S FAVORITE GARDENING TOOL?

D-RAKE.

/1

JOKES TOTAL: /4

TEEN 2 CONTINUE TO THE NEXT PAGE ➔

JOKES

WHAT IS A MOVER'S FAVORITE SPORT?

BOXING.

/1

WHY DID NO ONE BELIEVE THE ATOM'S STORIES?

HE SAID HE MADE UP EVERYTHING!

/1

WHAT DID THE MEAT ASK THE SAUCE?

"WILL YOU MARINATE ME?"

/1

WHAT DID ONE INSECT SAY TO THE OTHER WHEN HE SAW HIS NEW OUTFIT?

"LOOKING FLY!"

/1

JOKES TOTAL: _____ **/4**

TIME TO ADD UP YOUR POINTS! ➜

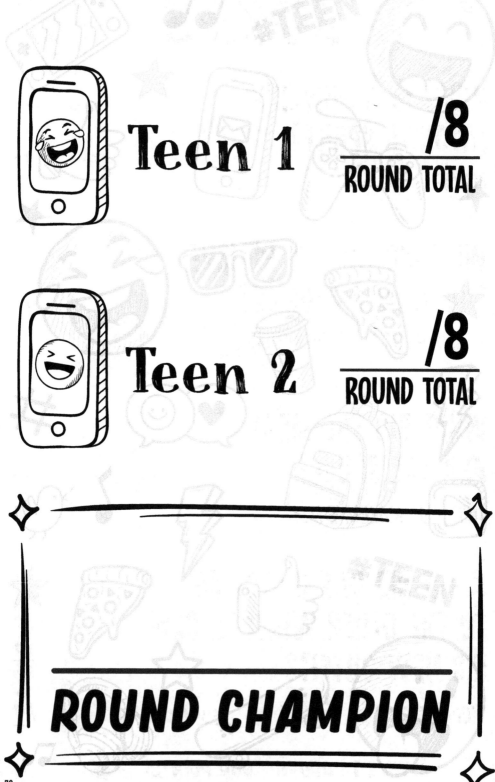

Teen 1 $\frac{}{\text{/8}}$ ROUND TOTAL

Teen 2 $\frac{}{\text{/8}}$ ROUND TOTAL

ROUND CHAMPION

ADD UP EACH PLAYER'S SCORE FROM
ALL PREVIOUS ROUNDS.
THE PLAYER WITH THE MOST POINTS IS CROWNED
THE ULTIMATE LAUGH MASTER!

IF POINTS RESULT IN A TIE,
MOVE ON TO THE TIE-BREAKER ROUND.

 **Teen 1**

GRAND TOTAL

Teen 2

GRAND TOTAL

THE ULTIMATE LAUGH MASTER

ROUND
11

TIE-BREAKER
(WINNER TAKES ALL!)

JOKES

WHY DO TEENS STILL WATCH CARTOONS?
IT'S CALLED ANIME!

/1

WHAT DAY OF THE WEEK NEVER LOSES?
WINS-DAY!

/1

WHY DID THANOS TAKE ON THE AVENGERS?
HE THOUGHT IT WOULD BE A SNAP!

/1

WHAT'S A GAMER'S LEAST FAVORITE LETTER?
/1

L.

JOKES TOTAL: /4

TEEN 1 CONTINUE TO THE NEXT PAGE →

JOKES

WHAT DO YOU CALL A CLOCK WITH INVOLUNTARY MOVEMENT?

TIKTOK.

/1

WHY DON'T TEENS HAVE BAGGY PANTS?

THEY LIKE TO "PULL UP."

/1

WHICH BOARD GAME IS TRENDING MOST?

WELL, CHECKERS ARE IN STYLE!

/1

WHAT DO YOU CALL AN AVOCADO THAT'S GOING DOWNHILL?

/1

GUAC 'N' ROLL.

JOKES TOTAL: /4

PASS THE BOOK TO TEEN 2 ➡️

JOKES

WHY WEREN'T THE TEENS SHOCKED WHEN THEY GOT IN TROUBLE?

_____ /1

THEY'RE ALREADY USED TO BEING GROUNDED!

WHAT DO YOU SAY TO MAKE SOMEONE BLOW UP?

_____ /1

"OK BOOMER."

WHY ARE COMPUTER KIDS SO OPEN-MINDED?

_____ /1

THEY'RE ALL ABOUT THAT PC!

WHO'S IN CHARGE OF THE WINTER SOLDIER AFTER HE JOINED THE AVENGERS?

_____ /1

NICK FLURRY.

JOKES TOTAL: _____ /4

TEEN 2 CONTINUE TO THE NEXT PAGE ➞

JOKES

WHY DID THE ALGEBRA TEACHER TRAVEL SOUTH?

ALL THE X'S LIVE IN TEXAS! _____ /1

WHAT DO YOU CALL A MONKEY FLYING A DIRIGIBLE?

A BLIMP-ANZEE! _____ /1

WHAT DO KIDS CHASE THAT'S INVISIBLE?

CLOUT! _____ /1

WHY DON'T THE AVENGERS LIKE SWIMMING WITH THE HULK?

HULK SPLASH! _____ /1

JOKES TOTAL: _____ /4

TIME TO ADD UP YOUR POINTS! ➡️

ADD UP EACH PLAYER'S SCORE FROM THE PREVIOUS ROUND.
THE PLAYER WITH THE MOST POINTS IS CROWNED THE ULTIMATE LAUGH MASTER!

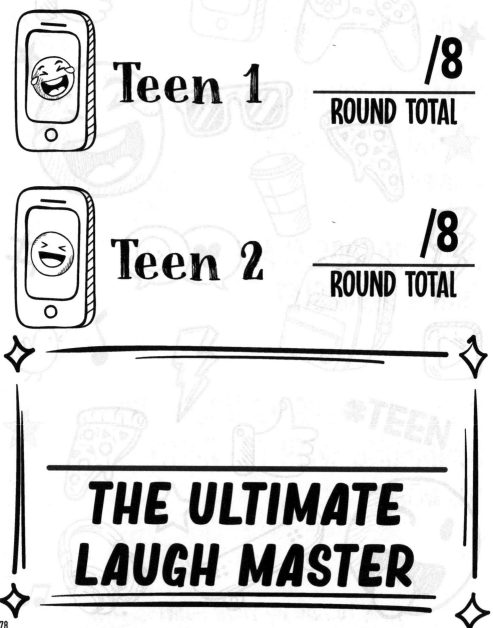

Teen 1 ___ **/8**
ROUND TOTAL

Teen 2 ___ **/8**
ROUND TOTAL

THE ULTIMATE LAUGH MASTER

CHECK OUT OUR

VISIT US AT
WWW.DONTLAUGHCHALLENGE.COM
TO CHECK OUT OUR NEWEST BOOKS!

OTHER JOKE BOOKS!

IF YOU HAVE ENJOYED OUR BOOK,
WE WOULD LOVE FOR YOU TO
KINDLY REVIEW US ON AMAZON!